WONDERS OF NATURE COLOURING BOOK

WONDERS OF NATURE COLOURING BOOK

This edition published in 2018 by Arcturus Publishing Limited
26/27 Bickels Yard, 151–153 Bermondsey Street,
London SE1 3HA

ISBN: 978-1-78888-850-9
CH005330NT
Supplier 29, Date 0918, Print run 7803

Printed in China

Created for children 10+

Introduction

Focusing your mind on a creative activity such as colouring can lift the spirits and calm the mind. Unwind and have fun with this beautiful collection of images from the natural world which includes line drawings of flowers, birds, animals and abstracts for you to complete as the mood takes you.

With a set of simple tools – coloured pens, pencils, felt-tips or markers – you can produce gorgeous artworks to treasure.

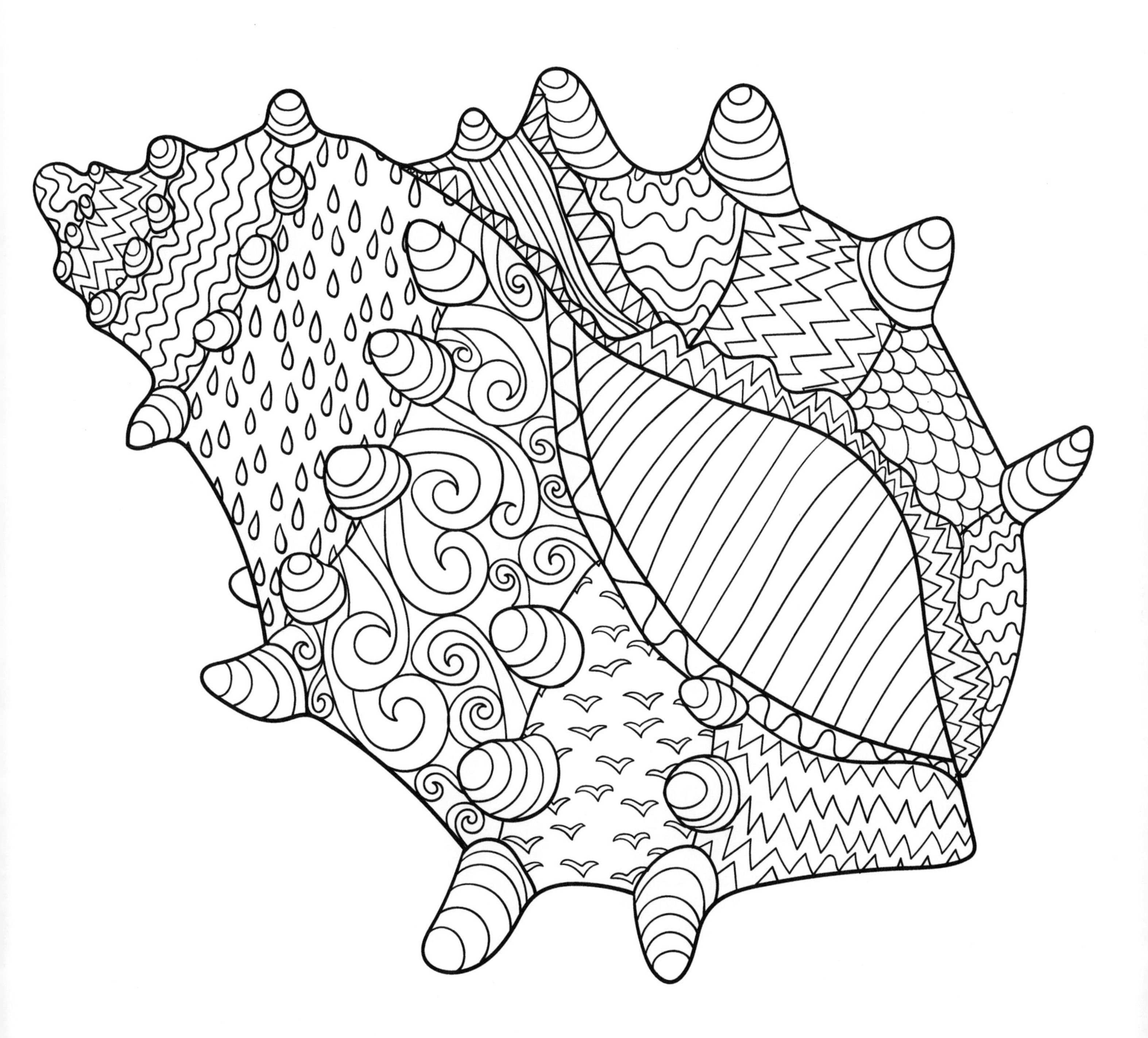